CHRIS DE BURGH
GREATEST HITS

GW00580099

WISE PUBLICATIONS
LONDON / NEW YORK / PARIS / SYDNEY / COPENHAGEN / MADRID / TOKYO

PATRICIA THE STRIPPER

WORDS & MUSIC BY CHRIS DE BURGH

4

A SPACEMAN CAME TRAVELLING

WORDS & MUSIC BY CHRIS DE BURGH

1. A space-man came trav - 'ling on his ship from a - far, 'twas
2. foll - owed a light and came down to a shed where a
3. stran - ger spoke he said do not fear I

la, la, la, la, la, la, la, la, la, la, la, la, la, la,

la, la, la, la, peace ___ and good will to all men ___

and love for the child.

La, la, la, la, la, la, la, la, la, la, la, la, la, la, la, la,

VERSE 4

This lovely music went trembling through the ground
And many were wakened on hearing sound
And trav'lers on the road the village they found
By the light of that ship in the sky which shone all around.

VERSE 5

And just before dawn at the paling of the sky
The stranger returned and said now I must fly
When two thousand years of your time has gone by
The song will begin once again to a baby's cry.

SATIN GREEN SHUTTERS

WORDS & MUSIC BY CHRIS DE BURGH

Where your love is put your heart,— guard these mo-ments well—

where your dreams are, put your hopes— you know they will not fail — you. When the

sun ri - ses__ in the morn - ing you will wake up and find __ her yawn - ing, when the

wind blows __ strong and cold she'll be with you un - til you grow old. __

Where your love is, put your heart. Oh what would you do
Where your love is, put your heart. Oh what would you do

if your dreams __ came true?
if your dreams __ came true?

When you're sad __ and feel - ing low, __ you're on your own __ with no -

- where to go. __ Make be - lieve __ that she is __ gone __ play your gui - tar __ and

write a song — for her. Write — down the words — a - bout

how you cried — when you woke up weep -ing 'cos you thought that she'd died, and you

heard her breath-ing through your pain, — and you held her close — and cried all ov - er a - gain —

D.%. al Coda

⊕ *CODA*

days.

SPANISH TRAIN
WORDS & MUSIC BY CHRIS DE BURGH

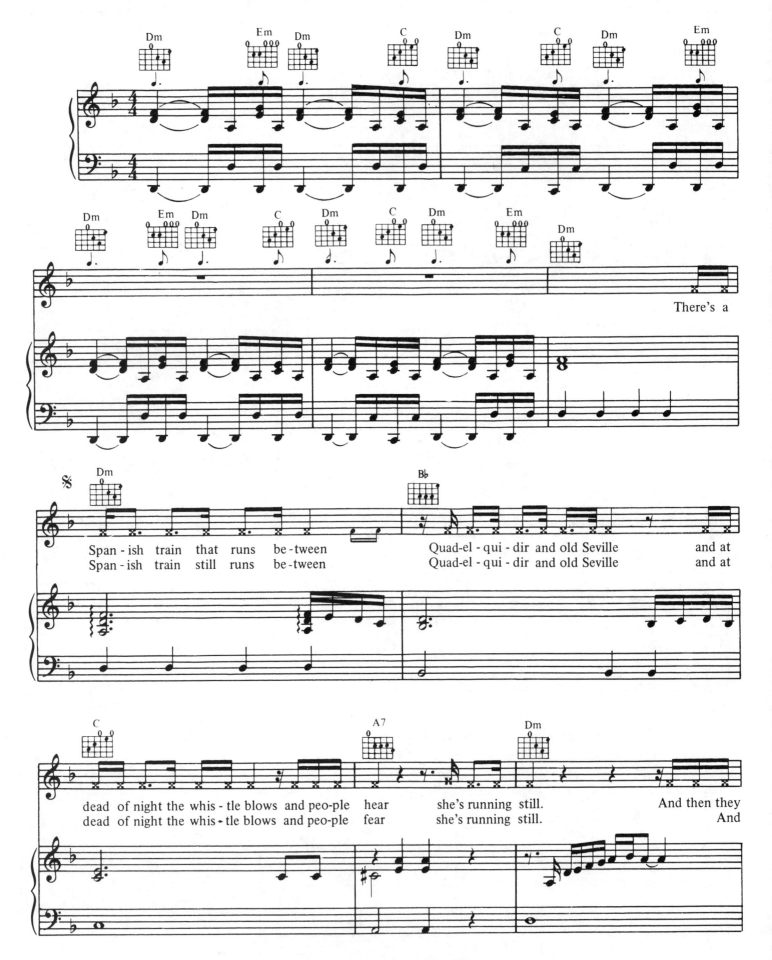

There's a

Span-ish train that runs be-tween / Quad-el-qui-dir and old Seville / and at
Span-ish train still runs be-tween / Quad-el-qui-dir and old Seville / and at

dead of night the whis-tle blows and peo-ple hear / she's running still. / And then they
dead of night the whis-tle blows and peo-ple fear / she's running still. / And

20

de-vil just grinned and said I may have sinned but there's no need to push me a - round, I
deal me one for the time has come to see who'll be King of this place, But

got here first so you can do your worst, he's going under ground. Well I
as he spoke from beneath his cloak he slipped another ace. Ten

think I'll give you one more chance said the de - vil with a smile, so
thou-sand souls was the open - ing bid, but soon went up to 59, but the

throw a - way that stu - pid lance. It's real - ly not your style,
Lord didn't see what the devil did and he said 'that suits me fine' I'll

jo-ker is the name,   po-ker is the game,   we'll play right here on this bed.   And
raise you high to 105   and for-ev-er put an end to your sin.   But the

then we'll bet for the big-gest stakes yet   the souls of the   dead.
devil let out a mighty shout.   My hand   wins.

CHORUS

And I said, look out ___ Lord he's gon-na win! ___ The
And I said, Lord, oh ___ Lord you let him win. ___ The

sun is down and the night's rid - ing in.   That train is dead on time, many
sun is down and the night's rid - ing in.   That train is dead on time, many

BORDERLINE

WORDS & MUSIC BY CHRIS DE BURGH

Lyrics:

I'm standing at the station I am waiting for a train___ to take me to the bor-der and my loved one far a-way I warned a bunch of sol-diers head-ing

see her there and I know I'll have to say good-bye a-gain
nev-er know how men can see the wis - dom in a war

And it's break-ing my heart I

know what I must do. I hear my country call me but I want to be with you I'm

No bor-der line_____

no bor-der line._____

rit.

DON'T PAY THE FERRYMAN

WORDS & MUSIC BY CHRIS DE BURGH

1. It was late at night on the op-en road. Speed-ing like a man on the run
Roam-ing mist then he gets on board, now there'-ll be no turn-ing back.

31

HIGH ON EMOTION

WORDS & MUSIC BY CHRIS DE BURGH

Oh my heart is spin-ning like a wheel on-ly she can see the
Oh my heart is burn-ing like a fire clos-er now and she is

way that I feel eyes are hold-ing right a-cross the room
breath-ing de-sire take my hand and give it all your light

high ex-plo-sion com-ing out of the blue Well here we go a-gain liv-ing
take com-mand I am your rhy-thm to-night

way_____ hey! ___   *Instrumental (Repeat x2)*

I am

high_____ on e-mo - tion_____   high_____ a - gain___

THE LADY IN RED

WORDS & MUSIC BY CHRIS DE BURGH

never seen so many men ask you if you want-ed to dance,
nev - er seen so ma - ny peo - ple want to be there by your side,

they're look-ing for a lit - tle ro - mance,
and when you turned to me and smiled, it

giv - en half a chance,
took my breath a - way, and I have

and I have

nev - er seen that dress you're wear - ing, or the
nev - er had such a feel - ing, such a

I'll ne - ver for - get

the way you look to - night.

2. I've way you look to - night,

I nev-er will__ for-get__
the way you look to-night.__
The la - dy in red,
my la - dy in red.

43

MISSING YOU

WORDS & MUSIC BY CHRIS DE BURGH

I've been miss-ing you. _____ (miss-ing you)

I've got the ro-ses, I've got the wine, with a lit-tle luck she will be
There is no rea-son to the things that we do, _____ you can break a heart with just a

here on time. This is the place we used to go with
word or two, and take a life-time to a-pol-og-ise.

ro-man-tic mu-sic and the lights _____ down low, _____ and as you stand there a-mazed at the
when the one you love's in front of your eyes, _____ and I will fall to my knees like a

door ___ and you're wond - 'ring what all this is for, ___ it's just a
fool ___ if it's the on - ly way of get - ting through, you see if

sim - ple thing from me to you, the la - dy that I a - dore, ___
I think you are beau - ti - ful, some - one else is gon - na feel it too,

'cause there's some - thing that you ___ should know, ___ it's that
so there's on - ly one thing ___ to do, ___ tell you that

I've been miss - ing ___ you ___ more than words ___ can say ___
I've been miss - ing ___ you ___ more than words ___ can say ___

and that I've ___ been think-ing a-bout it ev-'ry day, ___
and that I've ___ been think-ing a-bout it ev-'ry day. ___

and the time ___ we had ___ just danc-
Well to - night's ___ our night ___ for danc-

- ing nice ___ and slow, ___ and I ___ said now I've found ___
- ing nice ___ and slow ___ be - cause now I've found ___

___ you I'm nev- er let-ting go. ___
___ you I'm nev- er let-ting go. ___

EXCLUSIVE DISTRIBUTORS:
MUSIC SALES LIMITED
8/9 FRITH STREET, LONDON W1D 3JB, ENGLAND.

MUSIC SALES PTY LIMITED
120 ROTHSCHILD AVENUE,
ROSEBERY, NSW 2018, AUSTRALIA.

ORDER NO. AM970255
ISBN 0-7119-8833-1
THIS BOOK © COPYRIGHT 2001 BY WISE PUBLICATIONS.

COVER DESIGN BY PHIL GAMBRILL.
PHOTOGRAPH COURTESY OF
LONDON FEATURES INTERNATIONAL.
PRINTED IN GREAT BRITAIN.

YOUR GUARANTEE OF QUALITY:
AS PUBLISHERS, WE STRIVE TO PRODUCE EVERY
BOOK TO THE HIGHEST COMMERCIAL STANDARDS.
THIS BOOK HAS BEEN CAREFULLY DESIGNED TO MINIMISE AWKWARD
PAGE TURNS AND TO MAKE PLAYING FROM IT A REAL PLEASURE.
PARTICULAR CARE HAS BEEN GIVEN TO SPECIFYING
ACID-FREE, NEUTRAL-SIZED PAPER MADE FROM PULPS WHICH
HAVE NOT BEEN ELEMENTAL CHLORINE BLEACHED.
THIS PULP IS FROM FARMED SUSTAINABLE FORESTS AND WAS
PRODUCED WITH SPECIAL REGARD FOR THE ENVIRONMENT.
THROUGHOUT, THE PRINTING AND BINDING HAVE
BEEN PLANNED TO ENSURE A STURDY, ATTRACTIVE PUBLICATION
WHICH SHOULD GIVE YEARS OF ENJOYMENT.
IF YOUR COPY FAILS TO MEET OUR HIGH STANDARDS,
PLEASE INFORM US AND WE WILL GLADLY REPLACE IT.

MUSIC SALES' COMPLETE CATALOGUE DESCRIBES
THOUSANDS OF TITLES AND IS AVAILABLE IN FULL COLOUR
SECTIONS BY SUBJECT, DIRECT FROM MUSIC SALES LIMITED.
PLEASE STATE YOUR AREAS OF INTEREST AND SEND
A CHEQUE/POSTAL ORDER FOR £1.50 FOR POSTAGE TO:
MUSIC SALES LIMITED, NEWMARKET ROAD, BURY ST. EDMUNDS,
SUFFOLK IP33 3YB.

WWW.MUSICSALES.COM